BehiNd tHe STaff ROOM dooR

Brian Moses lives in a small Sussex village with his wife, his two daughters and several bad-tempered chickens. He writes and edits poetry and picture books for young people. In the past twenty years he has travelled extensively throughout the UK and abroad, presenting his poetry and percussion show in schools, libraries and at festivals. *Behind the Staffroom Door* is his fourth collection of poetry for Macmillan.

After fleeing the circus to follow a career in cartoons, **Chris Garbutt** has been fluttering mothlike around the bright lights of all the world's major cities, selling his funny pictures for spare change. All funds from this book will go towards a brand-new packet of shiny pencils.

Also by Brian Moses

Taking Out the Tigers

Poems by Brian Moses

The Works 2

Poems on every subject and for every occasion

Chosen by Brian Moses and Pie Corbett

The Secret Lives of Teachers

Poems chosen by Brian Moses

Aliens Stole My Underpants

Poems chosen by Brian Moses

Behind the STAFF ROOM dooR

the veRy beSt oF BRiaN MoseS

Illustrated by Chris Garbutt

MACMILLAN CHILDREN'S BOOKS

*This book is dedicated to my mother, Margaret (1919–2007),
with thanks for her love and support.*

First published 2007 by Macmillan Children's Books
a division of Macmillan Publishers Limited
20 New Wharf Road, London N1 9RR
Basingstoke and Oxford
Associated companies throughout the world
www.panmacmillan.com

ISBN 978-0-230-01541-8

3 5 7 9 8 6 4

A CIP catalogue record for this book is available from
the British Library.

Typeset by Nigel Hazle
Printed and bound in Great Britain by Mackays of Chatham plc, Kent

Contents

The Ghoul School Bus

The ghoul school bus
is picking up its cargo
of little horrors.

They must all be home
before first light, when today
turns into tomorrow.

All the sons and daughters of vampires,
little Igors and junior Fangs,
the teenage ghouls with their ghoulfriends
all wail as the bus bell clangs.

And the driver doesn't look well,
he's robed completely in black,
and the signboard says – Transylvania,
by way of hell and back.

The seats are slimy and wet,
there's a terrible graveyard smell,
all the small ghouls cackle and spit,
and practise their ghoulish spells.

The witches are reading their ABCs,
cackling over 'D' for disease,
while tomboy zombies are falling apart
and werewolves are checking for fleas.

When the bus slows down to drop them off
at Coffin Corner or Cemetery Gates,
their mummies are waiting to greet them
with eyes full of anguish and hate.

The ghoul school bus
is dropping off its cargo
of little horrors.

They must all be home
before first light, when today
turns into tomorrow.

Lovey-Dovey

When Dad and Mum go all lovey-dovey
we just don't know where to look.
My sister says, 'Cut it out, you two,'
while I stick my nose in a book.

Mum has this faraway look on her face
while Dad has a silly grin.
'Don't mind us, kids,' he says.
We just wish they'd pack it in.

Dad calls Mum, 'Little Sugarplum,'
and Mum says, 'You handsome brute.'
Dad laughs and says, 'Look at your mum,
don't you think that she's cute?

'I guess that's why I married her,
she's my truly wonderful one.'
Mum says he doesn't mean any of it
but she thinks he's a lot of fun.

I just can't stand all the kissing,
just who do they think they are?
I caught them once on our driveway,
snogging in the back of our car!

I hate it when they're lovey-dovey
but I hate it more when they fight,
when faces redden and tempers flare
and sharp words cut through the night.

So I'd rather they kissed and cuddled
and joked about and laughed.
At least we can tell everything's OK
when Mum and Dad are daft.

Names

My name is 'Couldn't care less',
just let the forests die.
My name is 'Can't be bothered',
who cares about holes in the sky?

My name is 'I'm too busy',
let someone else do the worrying.
There's nothing that I can do
if the ice caps are wearing thin.

My name is 'Leave me alone',
just don't go preaching to me.
Gossip is what I care about,
not oil that's spilt in the sea.

My name is 'I'm all right, Jack',
there's really no cause for alarm.
Hens are silly birds, who cares
if they suffer at the factory farm?

Who cares about global warming?
I like a spot of hot weather.
My name is 'Sit on the fence',
my name is 'All of a dither'.

So stop saying what I should think,
I don't want to believe what I'm told.
My name is 'Hope it will go away',
My name is 'Don't get involved'.

And who do you think you are,
telling us all we should worry?
WELL, MY NAME'S A WARNING FROM
FUTURE YEARS,
IT'S 'LISTEN OR YOU'LL BE SORRY'.

Croc City

Beneath the streets of New York
     there are sewers that stretch for miles.
They say the sewers of New York
     are filled with crocodiles
and alligators that frightened folk
     have just flushed down the pan
when the creatures stopped being babies
     and started snapping at their hands.

Croc City,
down below when the city sleeps,
croc city,
snapping away to a hip-hop beat,
croc city.

Pity the poor sewer worker
     taking his nightly stroll,
thinking about hot coffee
     at the end of his dark patrol.
Then out of the slime a snapper
     raises its ugly head,
how fast can you sprint down a sewer pipe
     when a crocodile wants you dead . . . ?

Croc City,
down below when the city sleeps,
croc city,
snapping away to a hip-hop beat,
croc city.

The State Department issues advice
      to those who find a croc:
whatever you do, don't go after it,
      don't chase it with a rock.
Don't start to think you're Dundee
      out to catch a snapper.
If he opens his mouth, then you can be sure
      this croc, he ain't no rapper!!

Croc City,
down below when the city sleeps,
croc city,
snapping away to a hip-hop beat,
croc city.

Croc City,
down below when the city sleeps,
croc city,
snapping away to a hip-hop beat,
croc city . . . YEAH!

Monster Crazy

Everyone here has gone Monster Crazy,
even those who are normally lazy,
binoculars raised, though the view may be hazy,
everyone here has gone Monster Crazy.

So come on, Nessie, give us a wave,
don't stay hidden in your underwater cave.
You're the talk of the town, the darling of the press,
it wouldn't be summer without you in Loch Ness.

Just come on up and prove that you're there,
sometime or other you must surface for air,
somebody's camera will photograph you,
proving, at last, if you're one hump or two!

Everyone here has gone Monster Crazy,
even those who are normally lazy,
binoculars raised, though the view may be hazy,
everyone here has gone Monster Crazy.

Just waggle your flipper or flip your tail,
make some fisherman's face turn pale
as you lift your head to look at the view,
there are hundreds waiting to interview you.

Just one word, Nessie, go on be a pet,
can't you stop playing hard to get?
You could be on TV, you'd have lots of money,
American tourists all calling you 'Honey'!

Everyone here has gone Monster Crazy,
even those who are normally lazy,
binoculars raised, though the view may be hazy,
everyone here has gone MONSTER CRAZY!

The Museum of Mythical Beasts

Go right in, past a beam of light
that shoots from a Cyclops' eye,
then put on armour and pick up a sword,
test how much of a hero you are:
only the bravest and best may steal the gold
from a griffin's nest.

Then try to resist a mermaid's song.
How long will you stay before you're forced
to block your ears and turn away?

Now braver souls have tangled with trolls,
they'll carry you off to be their slave.
Careful, don't trip, just a pile of old bones,
previous visitors, I suppose!

A date with Medusa! What a surprise!
Keep your head and don't look in her eyes.
Move forward once more till you reach a door.
The Minotaur is next on our list,
a horrible task, you'd be well advised
to go prepared when you visit his lair.

The terrible smell is the Gorgon of death;
run past, run fast, don't waste any time
in escaping the blast of its breath.

Beware the Roc that will snatch you away
as a plaything for one of her young
or the goblins already hung over their pans
or the two-headed ogre who can't decide
which mouth he should slide you in!

And now you head for the final test,
a dragon, so deadly, so dreadful, so strong.
Don't weaken at all when you hear her ROAR
as you score more points with Saint George.

Then at the exit, don't forget
to collect your certificate,
dated and signed to say you survived
the museum of mythical beasts.

Day Closure

We had a day closure on Monday
and I spent the morning in bed,
but the teachers went in as usual
and someone taught them instead.

And I thought of them all in the classroom
stuck to their seats in rows,
some of them sucking pen lids,
head teacher scratching his nose.

Perhaps it's a bit like an MOT
to check if teachers still know
the dates of our kings and queens
or the capital of so and so.

Perhaps they had tables and spellings,
did the head give them marks out of ten?
And then, if they got any wrong,
did he make them learn them again?

I thought of them out at breaktime
playing football or kiss chase or tag,
picking up teams in the playground
or scoffing crisps from a bag.

If I'd been a fly on the wall
I might have watched while they slaved,
I'd have seen who asked silly questions
or if anyone misbehaved.

I thought of them all going home,
crossing the road to their mums.
They looked very grim the next day.
It couldn't have been much fun.

All the Things You Can Say to Places in the UK

Always say 'Ta' to Leamington Spa,
say 'Have a nice day' to Whitley Bay.
You can shout 'What's new' or even 'Howdoo'
to inhabitants of Looe or Crewe.
You can tell the whole story in Tobermory,
say 'Hi' to Rye and 'Right on' to Brighton
or call out 'Let's go' to Plymouth Hoe.
Talk through your dreams in Milton Keynes,
say 'It's all for the best' in Haverfordwest.
Always say 'Yes' when you visit Skegness
but only say 'No' in Llandudno.
Don't tell a lie to the Isle of Skye
or say 'It smells' in Tunbridge Wells.
Don't talk rude if you're down in Bude
or start to get gabby in Waltham Abbey.
Don't ever plead in Berwick-upon-Tweed
or say 'You look ill' to Burgess Hill.
You could lose your voice and talk with your hands
when you take a trip to Camber Sands,
but whatever you say just won't impress
the residents of Shoeburyness.

At the Zoo

If you want to get married at London Zoo
this is what we can offer you . . .

A four-metre-long reticulated snake
gift-wrapped round your wedding cake.
A choir of hyenas singing loud,
a congregation of apes from rent-a-crowd.
Two charming chimps that will bridesmaid you
and if you need a witness use a kangaroo
at the zoo, at the zoo, at the zoo.

The waiters look great in their penguin suits,
the monkeys will serve you selected fruits.
The alligators are simply delighted,
even ocelots get quite excited.
The Vietnamese pot-bellied pigs
will take to their toes and dance wedding jigs
at the zoo, at the zoo, at the zoo.

The lions look forward to welcoming you
to your wedding breakfast here at the zoo,
and any leftovers they'd be pleased to chew
at the zoo, at the zoo, at the zoo.

Yes, we look forward to marrying you
at the zoo, at the zoo, at the zoo.

What Teachers Wear in Bed

It's anybody's guess
what teachers wear in bed at night,
so we held a competition
to see if any of us were right.

We did a spot of research,
although some of them wouldn't say,
but it's probably something funny
as they look pretty strange by day.

Our head teacher's quite old fashioned,
he wears a Victorian nightshirt,
our sports teacher wears her tracksuit
and sometimes her netball skirt.

That new teacher in the infants
wears bedsocks with see-through pyjamas,
our deputy head wears a T-shirt
he brought back from the Bahamas.

We asked our secretary what she wore
but she shooed us out of her room,
and our teacher said her favourite nightie
and a splash of expensive perfume.

And Mademoiselle, who teaches French,
is really very rude,
she whispered, '*Alors!* Don't tell a soul,
but I sleep in the . . . back bedroom!'

The Lost Angels

In a fish tank in France
we discovered the lost angels,
fallen from heaven and floating now
on imaginary tides.
And all along the sides of the tank,
faces peered, leered at them,
laughing, pouting,
pointing, shouting,
while hung above their heads, a sign,
'Ne pas plonger les mains dans le bassin,'
Don't put your hands in the tank –
the turtles bite seriously.
And who can blame them,
these creatures with angels' wings,
drifting past like alien craft?
Who knows what signals they send
through an imitation ocean,
out of sight of sky,
out of touch with stars?

Dream on, lost angels,
then one day, one glorious day,
you'll flap your wings
and fly again.

Parent-Free Zone

Parents, please note
that from now on
our room is
a 'Parent-Free Zone'.

There will be no spying
under the pretence
of tidying up.

There will be no banning
of television programmes
because our room
is a tip,

no complaints about noise,
or remarks about the ceiling
caving in.

No disturbing the dirty clothes
that have festered in piles
for weeks.

No removal of coffee cups
where green mould
has taken a hold.
(These have been left there
for scientific-research purposes.)

No reading of letters
to gain unauthorized information
that may be used against us
at a later date.

No searching through school bags
to discover if we've done our homework
or unearth forgotten notes.

Our room is a 'Parent-Free Zone'
and a notice is pinned to the door.

But just a minute,
there's something wrong . . .

MUM – WHY HAVEN'T YOU MADE OUR
    BEDS?

Shopping Trolley

Scoot down the aisles
in my shopping trolley,
I could go for miles
in my shopping trolley.

Never say excuse me,
never say please,
ram it in the back
of someone's knees.

You really won't
believe your eyes,
my shopping trolley's
been customized.

It's got bull bars,
radio controls,
engine in the back
and it purrs like a Rolls.

It's got a Volvo chassis,
a velvet seat,
and around the store
it can't be beat.

It does somersaults
and big backflips,
roly-polys
and wheelie dips.

It does over seventy
miles per hour,
flashing past
in a burst of power.

Scoot down the aisles
in my shopping trolley,
I could go for miles
in my shopping trolley.

Never say excuse me,
never say please,
ram it in the back
of someone's knees.

Aliens Stole My Underpants

To understand the ways
of alien beings is hard,
and I've never worked it out
why they landed in my backyard.

And I've always wondered why
on their journey from the stars,
these aliens stole my underpants
and took them back to Mars.

They came on a Monday night
when the weekend wash had been done,
pegged out on the line
to be dried by the morning sun.

Mrs Driver from next door
was a witness at the scene
when aliens snatched my underpants –
I'm glad that they were clean!

It seems they were quite choosy
as nothing else was taken.
Do aliens wear underpants
or were they just mistaken?

I think I have a theory
as to what they wanted them for,
they needed to block off a draught
blowing in through the spacecraft door.

Or maybe some Mars museum
wanted items brought back from space.
Just think, my pair of Y-fronts
displayed in their own glass case.

And on the label beneath
would be written where they got 'em
and how such funny underwear
once covered an Earthling's bottom!

Behind the Staffroom Door

Ten tired teachers slumped in the staffroom at
    playtime,
one collapsed when the coffee ran out, then there were
    nine.

Nine tired teachers making lists of things they hate,
one remembered playground duty, then there were
    eight.

Eight tired teachers thinking of holidays in Devon,
one slipped off to pack his case, then there were seven.

Seven tired teachers weary of children's tricks,
one hid in the stock cupboard, then there were six.

Six tired teachers under the weather, barely alive,
one gave an enormous sneeze, then there were five.

Five tired teachers gazing at the open door,
one made a quick getaway, then there were four.

Four tired teachers, faces lined with misery,
one locked herself in the ladies, then there were three.

Three tired teachers wondering what to do,
one started screaming when the bell rang, then there
    were two.

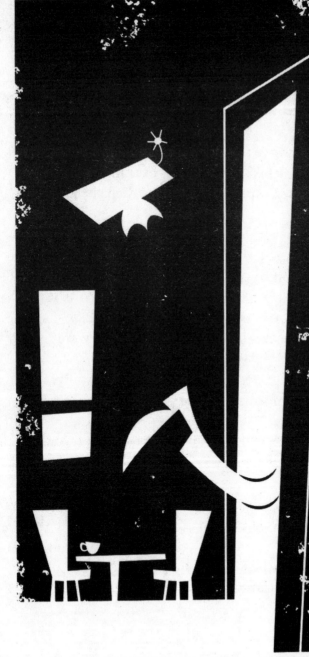

Two tired teachers thinking life really ought to be fun,
one was summoned to see the Head, then there was
    one.

One tired teacher caught napping in the afternoon
    sun,
fled quickly from the staffroom, then there were none.

Elephants Can't Jump

Elephants can't jump, and that's a fact.
So it's no good expecting an elephant to jump for joy
if you tell him some good news.
You won't make an elephant jump
if you sound a loud noise behind him –
elephants can't jump.
You won't see an elephant skipping or pole-vaulting.
It wasn't an elephant that jumped over the moon
when the little dog laughed,
and contrary to popular belief
elephants do not jump when they see mice.
Elephants, with their great bulk,
don't like to leave the ground.
Elephants and jumping do not go well together.

And perhaps it's all for the best,
for if elephants did jump, just think
of all the trouble they'd cause.
If all the elephants in Africa linked trunks
and jumped together,
their combined weight on landing
would cause a crack in the Earth's crust.
Just think if elephants were jumping for joy
every time they won the lottery
or welcomed baby elephants into the world,
they'd probably have a knock-on effect
and all the rest of us would shoot skywards
when they landed.

I'm rather pleased to discover that elephants can't
    jump . . .
The world suddenly seems that tiny bit safer.

Entering a Castle

Don't enter a castle quietly
    or timidly.
Don't enter it anxiously,
    ready to bolt
    at the slightest sound.
Don't enter it stealthily,
    taking slow and thoughtful steps,
    considering with each footfall
    the mystery of history.
Don't be meek
    or frightened to speak.
For when you enter a castle
you should *charge* through the gate
and signal your arrival with a **SHOUT!**
You should play the invading army
and **barge** a way through.
You should *swagger* up to the door
    then **shove** it aside and announce,
    'Here I am! This is mine!'

This castle is here, it is waiting for you,
  and today,
    it is yours for the taking!

Days

Days fly by on holidays,
they escape like birds
released from cages.
What a shame you can't buy
tokens of time, save them up
and lengthen the good days,
or maybe you could tear out time
from days that drag, then pay it back
on holidays, wild days,
days you wish would last forever.
You could wear these days with pride,
fasten them like poppies to your coat,
or keep them in a tin, like sweets,
a confection of days
to be held on the tongue
and tasted, now and then.

Lost Magic

Today I found some lost magic –
a twisty-twirly horn
of a unicorn lying at my feet.
And when I stopped
to pick it up, to hold it
in my fist, I remembered
how once upon a time
you could always find unicorns,
but there are no unicorns now.

You would find them on the shoreline,
flitting in and out of caves in cliffs,
or climbing hills at twilight.
They would lead you through forests,
sometimes hiding behind trees,
and if you lost them or they lost you,
you could always find them again,
but there are no unicorns now.

And it didn't matter
if you followed them all day,
the edge of the world was miles away,
there was nothing to fear.
And none of the unicorns we knew ever
changed into dangerous strangers.

Once upon a time there were unicorns,
but there are no unicorns now.

Four-Second Memory

Is it a fact or is it a hype
that a goldfish suffers a memory wipe
every time four seconds passes by
and if it's true, does he wonder why?
Perhaps that's why he's happy to swim
round and round in his tank, nothing bothers him.
Four seconds and then his mind is wiped clean,
four seconds and he's no idea where he's been.
So every circuit's a different view,
every circuit brings something new.
Does he ever get feelings of déjà vu
or say to another fish, 'Don't I know you,
haven't we met some place before?'
But after four seconds the slam of a door
erases the thought from his memory bank
and he'll take another tour of his tank.

In a goldfish world there could never be
any sense of goldfish history.
They would never follow serials on TV,
their lives must be one big mystery –
What did I do, what have I seen,
who did I meet, where have I been?
Do they suffer four seconds of stress,
could one ever be called as a witness?
'Where were you on the night of the crime?'
He'd really have no notion of time.
Adrift in the water, he's floating and flowing
with only four seconds to know where he's going,
four seconds and then his mind is wiped clean
and the goldfish has no idea where he's been.

The Ssssnake Hotel

An Indian python will welcome you
to the Ssssnake hotel.
As he finds your keys he'll maybe enquire
if you're feeling well.
And he'll say that he hopes
you survive the night,
that you sleep without screaming
and don't die of fright
at the Ssssnake hotel.

There's an anaconda that likes to wander
the corridors at night,
and a boa that will lower itself on to guests
as they search for the light.
And if by chance you lie awake
and nearby something hisses,
I warn you now, you're about to be covered
with tiny vipery kisses
at the Ssssnake hotel.

And should you hear a chorus of groans
coming from the room next door,
and the python cracking someone's bones,
please don't go out and explore.
Just ignore the screams
and the strangled yells
when you spend a weekend
at the Ssssnake hotel.

Dragons' Wood

We didn't see dragons
in Dragons' Wood
but we saw
where the dragons had been.

We saw tracks in soft mud
that could only have been scratched
by some sharp-clawed creature.

We saw scorched earth
where fiery dragon breath
had whitened everything to ash.

We saw trees burnt to charcoal.
We saw dragon dung
rolled into boulders.

And draped from a branch
we saw sloughed off skin,
scaly, still warm . . .

We didn't see dragons
in Dragons' Wood
but this was the closest
we'd ever been

to believing.

The Shouting Side

There's a war being waged
in our family,
Mum versus Dad,
in the middle there's me
and it's hard to decide
whose side I'm on
when they're both
on the shouting side.

Dad shouts at Mum,
Mum screams at Dad,
then they start on me
and it makes me mad,
I don't want to decide
whose side I'm on
when they're both
on the shouting side.

Can't they see,
can't they be quiet?
Why do they yell
like they're starting a riot?
They're acting this out
on a tiny stage,
there's no need to shout
or fly into a rage.

There's no need to take out
their feelings on me,
I'm trying to listen,
can't they see?
I'm standing here
with my ears wide open,
somebody please
be quietly spoken.

There's a war being waged
in our family,
Mum versus Dad,
in the middle there's me
and it's hard to decide
whose side I'm on
when they're both
on the shouting side.

Cup Final Day 1961

Pete supported Burnley,
but Spurs were all that I cared about.
We knew, by the end of Cup Final day
that one of us would be leaping about
and one of us would be quiet,
unless, of course, it went to a replay.

So that Saturday in May
we sat down to watch
the match of the year.

And Spurs got off to a dream start
when Jimmy Greaves scored an early goal
and I was ecstatic
till Pete knocked me back. 'Sit down,'
he said, 'shut up, watch the match.'

It was nothing much till the second half,
then Burnley scored and Pete went mad,
but just as he sat back down again
it was Bobby Smith with a cracker of a goal
for Spurs. 'Don't shout so much,'
my mother called, 'the teams can't hear you.'

Then just ten minutes before the end
Branchflower booted a penalty
and Spurs stayed in front 3–1.
I leaped around, jumped up and down,

ran round the room holding the cup,
listened to the sound of the Wembley crowd
as I took my victory lap.

47

'You're daft, you are, you're crazy,' Pete said,
but I jeered him all the way to the door.
'Three–one,' I crowed, 'I told you so,'

then, 'What shall we do tomorrow?' I called,
but he didn't turn round, just walked away,
and next day too, it was like a wall
had suddenly grown between us.

He kept it up for a week or so,
wouldn't speak, kept clear of me,
and it took me a week to understand
that a game of ball didn't matter at all,
it's friendship that really counts.

So I went across and knocked on Pete's door.
'I'm sorry that your team lost,' I said.
He shrugged. 'Doesn't matter any more,
there's always next year, we'll beat you
for sure.'

'I expect so,' I said,
fingers crossed
behind my back.

December Moon

The moon has come out too soon,
it's still the middle of the afternoon
and the day shows no sign of darkness.

What is the moon doing,
sneaking into the sky when it's light?

What is the moon playing at?
Couldn't it sleep?
Has its alarm clock rung too soon?

Do we see the moon this early
in June or September?

Or does December bring a special moon,
a let's-get-these-nights-over-soon moon,
a can't-wait-for-Christmas-to-come moon?

The Hate

We began each morning with hymns.
'Lots of wind,' our teacher called
as she wrestled a melody
from the ancient hall piano.

Then we sat and gazed at the front
while the football results were read
and Donald was led in, held by the arm,
a look of alarm on his face.
I didn't know what he'd done,
perhaps he'd stolen or two-fingered
once too often. It must have been serious
in the eyes of God, in the eyes
of our headmistress.

She seemed to think
that boys' backsides were meant to be whacked,
but Donald struggled and lay on the floor
and flapped like a fish out of water.
Even the toughies were terrified
as the slipper rose and fell
a total of eighteen times till it stopped
and Donald stayed locked to the floor.

The piano was open but no one played
as we filed out silently and found our maths.
It stayed on our minds for much of the day,
but Donald wouldn't say what he'd done,
just shook his head and said nothing.

Our teacher said Donald would be forgiven,
start once again and clean the slate;
but I glimpsed him next day in prayers,
a dreadful look on his face, and I knew
it would take more than Jesus
to wipe away the hate.

Love Letter from Mary Tudor to Her Husband, Philip of Spain

(Spot the anachronism – an object in its wrong time!)

Dear Philip, my Phil,
it's making me ill
to think that
you don't love me.
I love you, my dear,
but you're making it clear
that this marriage
was not meant to be.

I'm here all alone,
if only you'd phone,
send a pigeon
or simply just write.
Invite me, please do,
Ibiza with you
would soon set
our marriage alight.

Dear Philip, my love,
my sweet turtle dove,
I know it's with you
I relate.
I wish you'd return
and help me to burn
all those plotting
against the state.

Everybody I know
says you should go,
but I need you
to give me an heir.
Do you think that I'm neater
than a sweet señorita
or do your eyes
wander elsewhere?

Dear Philip, I'm willing
to share double billing,
if our love could be
reignited.
Then our reign as one
will be equal to none,
King and Queen of
two countries united.

So Philip, my Phil,
come home, say you will,
without you it's really
quite scary.
Forsake sunny Spain
for the cold English rain
and the arms of
your loving wife, Mary.

xxxx

Billy's Coming Back

Word is out on the street tonight,
Billy's coming back.

There's a sound outside of running feet,
somebody somewhere's switched on the heat,
policemen are beating a swift retreat
now Billy's coming back.

Only last year when he went away
everyone heaved a sigh,
now news is out, and the neighbourhood
is set to blow sky-high.

Words are heard in the staffroom,
teachers' faces deepen with gloom,
can't shrug off this feeling of doom
now Billy's coming back.

It was wonderful when he upped and left,
a carnival feeling straight away,
no looking over shoulders,
each day was a holiday.

And now like a bomb no one dares to defuse,
time ticks on while kids quake in their shoes,
no winners here, you can only lose
now Billy's coming back.

It's dog eat dog on the street tonight,
it's cat and mouse, Billy's looking for a fight,
so take my advice, keep well out of sight
now Billy's coming back.

A Feather from an Angel

Anton's box of treasures held
a silver key and a glassy stone,
a figurine made of polished bone
and a feather from an angel.

The figurine was from Borneo,
the stone from France or Italy,
the silver key was a mystery
but the feather came from an angel.

We might have believed him if he'd said
the feather fell from a bleached white crow
but he always replied, 'It's an angel's, I know,
a feather from an angel.'

We might have believed him if he'd said,
'An albatross let the feather fall.'
But he had no doubt, no doubt at all,
his feather came from an angel.

I thought I'd dreamt him one night,' he'd say,
'but in the morning I knew he'd been there;
he left a feather on my bedside chair,
a feather from an angel.'

And it seems that all my life I've looked
for that sort of belief that nothing could shift,
something simple yet precious as Anton's gift,
a feather from an angel.

The Weirdest Exhibit

The museum galleries
go on for miles,
you see furniture and furnishings,
tapestries and tiles.
You see kitchens where fire grates
are blackened with soot,
but the weirdest exhibit
is a mummified foot.

It's gruesome and gross
but you'll love it the most,
the Egyptian mummified foot.

You can see right inside
where the skin has been ripped,
then you'll notice the bone
and the way it's been chipped.
And beneath the bandage
you'll see actual flesh . . .
I bet it smelt cheesy
even when it was fresh!

It's gruesome and gross
but you'll love it the most,
the Egyptian mummified foot.

And what's so amazing,
what's really fantastic,
the toenails are real
and not made of plastic.
And beneath the nails
you can see grains of sand.
Are they picked at each night
by a mummified hand?

It's gruesome and gross
but you'll love it the most,
the Egyptian mummified foot.

Cakes in the Staffroom

Nothing gets teachers more excited
than cakes in the staffroom at breaktime.
Nothing gets them more delighted
than the sight of plates
piled high with jammy doughnuts
or chocolate cake.

It's an absolute stampede
as the word gets round quickly,

and it's, 'Oooh these are really delicious,'
and, 'Aaah these doughnuts are ace.'

And you hear them say, 'I really shouldn't,'
or, 'Just a tiny bit, I'm on a diet.'

Really, it's the only time teachers are quiet,
when they're cramming cakes into their mouths,
when they're wearing a creamy moustache,
or the jam squirts out like blood,
or they're licking chocolate
from their fingers.

You can tell when they've been scoffing,
they get lazy in literacy,
sleepy in silent reading,
nonsensical in numeracy
and look guilty in assembly.

But nothing gets teachers more excited
than cakes in the staffroom at breaktime,
unless of course
it's wine in the staffroom at lunchtime!

Taking Out the Tigers

At twilight time
or early morning
a tiger-sized ROAR
is a fearsome warning
as a huge cat swaggers
through a fine sea mist,
its paws the size
of a boxer's fist,

when they're
taking out the tigers
on Sandown beach.

These tough kitties
have something to teach
about the law of the jungle
on Sandown beach.
And any kind of dog
would be most unwise
to challenge a cat
that's this sort of size,

when they're
taking out the tigers
on Sandown beach.

As a weak sun sinks
in a winter sky,
it reflects in the jewel
of a tiger's eye,
but the Indian Ocean
is dreams away
from the chilly surf
of Sandown Bay,

when they're
taking out the tigers
on Sandown beach,
taking out the tigers
on Sandown beach,
taking out the tigers . . .

Walking with My Iguana

I'm walking (I'm walking)
with my iguana (with my iguana)

I'm walking (I'm walking)
with my iguana (with my iguana)

When the temperature rises
to above eighty-five,
my iguana is looking
like he's coming alive.

So we make it to the beach,
my iguana and me,
then he sits on my shoulder
as we stroll by the sea

and I'm walking (I'm walking)
with my iguana (with my iguana)

I'm walking (I'm walking)
with my iguana (with my iguana)

Well, if anyone sees us
we're a big surprise,
my iguana and me
on our daily exercise,

till somebody phones
the local police
and says I have an alligator
tied to a leash

when I'm walking (I'm walking)
with my iguana (with my iguana)

I'm walking (I'm walking)
with my iguana (with my iguana)

It's the spines on his back
that make him look grim,
but he just loves to be tickled
under his chin.

And I know that my iguana
is ready for bed
when he puts on his pyjamas
and lays down his sleepy head

and I'm walking (I'm walking)
with my iguana (with my iguana)

still walking (still walking)
with my iguana (with my iguana)

With my iguana . . .

with my iguana . . .

and my piranha,

and my chihuahua,

and my chinchilla,

and my gorilla,

my caterpillar . . .

and I'm walking . . .

with my iguana . . .

Playing with Stars

Young children know what it's like
to play with stars.

First of all it's a wink and a smile
from some distant constellation,
then it's hide and seek as they disappear
in a cover of cloud.
Sometimes children see how far
they can travel to a star
before familiar voices call them
home to bed.

Like all good games, of course,
you need to use a little imagination
when playing with stars.
More experienced players
can jump over stars
or shake down a star.
Some can trap them in butterfly nets,
but you should always let them loose again.
Stars grow pale and die if you cage them.

Sometimes the stars tell stories
of their journeys across the sky
and sometimes they stay silent.
At these times children may travel themselves,
wandering a line that unravels

through their dreams.
At these times too the stars play their own games,
falling from the sky when there's no one there
to catch them.

Sometimes you find these stars on the ground,
dazed and confused. Be warned though,
even fallen stars may be hot to touch.

Young children know what it's like
to rescue stars, to hold them gently
in gloved hands and then,
with one almighty fling,
sling them back to the sky.

Adults forget what it's like
to play with stars,
and when children offer to teach them
they're far too busy.

Dear Yuri

Dear Yuri, I remember you,
the man with the funny name
who the Russians sent into space,
were you desperate for fame?

There surely must have been safer ways
to get into the history books,
perhaps you couldn't rock like Elvis
or you hadn't got James Dean's looks.

Perhaps you couldn't fight like Ali
or make a political speech,
so they packed you into a spaceship
and sent you out of Earth's reach.

And, Yuri, what was it like
to be way out there in space,
the first to break free of Earth's gravity
and look down on the human race?

I'd been doing my maths all morning,
and at lunchtime I heard what you'd done.
I told everyone back at school
how you'd rocketed near to the sun.

And, Yuri, I wanted to say
that I remember your flight,
I remember your name, Gagarin,
and the newsreel pictures that night.

And you must have pep-talked others
when they took off into the blue.
I've forgotten their names but, Yuri,
I'll always remember you.

Kirk Deighton

Kirk Deighton?
That can't be the name of a place!
Sounds more like the name
of a superhero, a '00' agent,
someone to swoon over.
Kirk Deighton,
suave, sophisticated,
a gold-plated gun in a
shoulder holster,
hairy chest, bullet-proof
vest.
The kind of guy that
girls adore,
a secret spy on a
dangerous mission
somewhere off the A1,
South Yorkshire.

YORKSHIRE

White Horse

As a child I dreamed
a white horse would come
and carry me away.
Not that my childhood was unhappy,
it was just that my small-boy head
was full of adventures.
The horse was a noble beast,
perhaps a unicorn
in a previous existence,
an elemental creature
of ice and fire,
with a mane like a shower of stars.

I believed I had only to wish for the horse
and we'd flee over fields
to the sea, or rescue princesses
with long-flowing dresses
before galloping a path to the clouds.
And there were those moments
when the sky conjured up
a rainbow bridge,
where we may have passed
from this world to another.

Later I discovered
that the white horse
wasn't rooted in childhood.
I came to realize
it had often been with me.
All those occasions
I'd wished to escape
and then found it.
All those times I'd flown
without knowing
I was riding the white horse's back.

Till now, with a different view
from a different house,
a white horse
paces the field beyond my window.
It seems to recognize in me
some previous complicity.
We were partners once,
we flew as one,
past the rim of what we knew
and out along the edges of dreams.

Missing – Grey and White Cat, Answers to the Name of Freddy

Why is it
I find it hard to believe
that Freddy will come
when you call?
Even if you threw open your windows
and bawled out his name,
not once, not twice,
but for a full fifteen minutes
of neighbourhood fame,
I just don't think that Freddy
will answer.

Cats roam, we know.
Cats find a welcoming mat
on the sunnier side of the road.
He'll have his paws
tucked under someone else's table
by now.
Or maybe he's eloped
with some cat he duetted with
on the corner one night.
Maybe she turned his head,
poor Fred, he's hooked by now,
couldn't come back
if he wanted to.

So it's no good
you putting up posters
all over Camden Town,
for even if you bawl and yell
each night for a week,
you may find an Eddie
or even a Teddy
trying your cat flap for size.
But whatever answers
won't be Freddy.
You can bet nine lives
that Freddy is gone
till he's ready
to stroll back home.

The Phantom Kiss

There's a phantom kiss on the loose,
you could find it in your house.
It flits about like a fly,
it scuttles about like a mouse.
It hides in gloomy corners
till someone turns out the light,
so you won't be able to see it
in the darkness of the night.
But the phantom kiss will be there
and you won't hear it speak your name,
but if it calls and it touches you,
you will never be the same!

Like a vampire that turns you into its own,
the phantom kiss will claim you.
Just a gentle brush of lips on your cheek
is all that it takes to inflame you.
You'll be wanting to kiss
everyone you see,
be it greatest friend
or deepest enemy.

If the phantom kiss
holds you in its power,
you won't shrug it off
in a minute or an hour.
It will hold you tight
in its embarrassing grip
while you kiss all around you
on cheek or on lips.

So remember if your mum's
always kissing you,
you'll realize now
that she was touched too.
And serial kissers
like your aunts and your gran,
you'll realize this
was how they began.

And someone who may have been touched too
is the person sitting next to you . . .

Fireflies

(From the Observatory of the Empire State Building)

The guidebooks all said
the views were stupendous,
the moment momentous,
the light show tremendous,
but no one mentioned
the fireflies.

But the fireflies
are what I remember the most,
that aerial ballet of tiny sparks
that dipped and danced
and lit up the dark,
that hung a string of fairy lights
in the sky above Manhattan.

And the light that flamed
from the streets below,
from the beating heart
of this electric city . . .
I wondered how many fireflies
it took, to stoke up the glow
and keep it burning.

I never expected fireflies,
but then, New York's like that.

If Houses Went on Holiday

Wouldn't it be great
if when you went on holiday,
your house could go on holiday too?
Whole terraces could disappear together
for boozy weekends in Ibiza.
Semi-detacheds could rekindle romance
side by side on moonlit beaches.
You'd find bungalows backpacking
and chalets criss-crossing the Channel.
Detached houses going solo,
seeking dates or mates on singles trips,
while apartment blocks could take package tours,
jetting to Jamaica in jumbos.

Just imagine houses hitting the holiday trail,
forming orderly queues on major roads
then crowding holiday beaches.
Imagine houses surfing or sunbathing,
jumping into swimming pools, keeping cool.
See them paragliding or rock-climbing,
scuba-diving or horse-riding.
So much better than brooding, silent and empty,
rooms filled with gloom, windows
like sad eyes, blinking back tears.
How much better it would be for houses
to have a holiday break like us!

The Food Obstacle Race

(With thanks to Sophie Roberts and Linette Moses)

For school sports day this year,
how about trying something different –

Try skipping with spaghetti
  or leaping through lasagne,
diving into doughnuts
  or cartwheeling in ketchup.

Try jumping into jelly
  or battling through bolognese,
somersaulting into sultanas
  or zooming through zabaglione.

Try rowing through rice pudding
  or making waves in mayonnaise,
weightlifting watermelons
  or tiptoeing through tagliatelle.

Try pole-vaulting with pepperoni
  or bouncing on boiled eggs,
stepping in salsa sauce
  or sprinting through salad cream.

And then you should see if your teachers
are up for this challenge too.
The teachers' race will be much more fun
if they do this event just like you!

There's a Hamster
in the Fast Lane

The speed cameras are flashing
but they can't identify
a hamster in the fast lane
as he roly-polys by.

He doesn't show a number
and shades obscure his eyes.
Police reports all tell of some
boy racer in disguise.

For everyone who sees him
he's the cause of mirth and mayhem.
He's passing big fat four-wheel drives
by rolling underneath them.

No more tickles on the tummy,
no more crummy little cage.
One hundred miles an hour at least,
fuelled by hamster rage.

He's passing open tops,
he's passing executive cars.
His energy is endless,
no sleep till Zanzibar!

He's belting down the bypass
like a speed king on a track,
unsure of where he's going
but he knows he won't be back!

Dreams of Garden Gnomes

The first garden gnome wants to drive a car.
The second garden gnome wants to play the guitar,
        to be a star, be on MTV.
The third garden gnome wants to shop frantically.
The fourth garden gnome has only one wish,
        that the rod in his hand might one day catch a
                fish.
The fifth garden gnome wants to fall in love.
The sixth garden gnome just wishes the dove
        that sits on his head would go away.
The seventh garden gnome wants a holiday.
The eighth garden gnome just wants to attack
        the stinky-poo cat that lives over the back,
        that calls round each evening to leave its mark.
The ninth garden gnome wants to glow in the dark.
The tenth garden gnome wants a lottery win.
The eleventh garden gnome wants to make a din
        by playing the drums, that's his big dream.
The twelfth wants to manage a football team.

But their destiny, all garden gnomes know,
is to stand about in the rain and the snow.
And although dreams flit through their heads with
                ease,
most slip away again with the breeze.